Tackling work-related
stress

SUPPORT

RELATIONSHIPS

CONTROL

CULTURE

CHANGE

DEMANDS

INDIVIDUAL

ROLE

TRAINING

CHECK FOR LEAFLET
AT FRONT OF BOOK

A managers' guide
to improving and maintaining
employee health and well-being

This guidance is issued by the Health and Safety Executive.
Following the guidance is not compulsory and you are free to take
other action. But if you do follow the guidance you will normally be
doing enough to comply with the law. Health and safety inspectors
seek to secure compliance with the law and may refer to this
guidance as illustrating good practice.

Contents

Preface

The Health and Safety Commission has a strategy for tackling work-related stress. The strategy has four key elements:

● to work with partners to develop clear, agreed standards of good management practice for a range of work-related stressors. These standards will cover issues connected to demands, control, support, role, relationships and change. The first ones will be published in 2003. Later in the guide we tell you what you can do now to start addressing some of these issues in your unit (see paragraphs 48–86);

● to better equip enforcement officers to handle the issue in their routine work;

● to facilitate a comprehensive approach to managing work-related stress; and

● a publicity drive to help educate employers. This guide forms part of that drive, but will be replaced with specific guidance once the standards have been developed.

Securing Health Together

The strategy we are developing for work-related stress adopts the principles of *'Securing Health Together'*[1] – a long-term occupational health strategy for England, Scotland and Wales. This forms a key plank of *'Revitalising Health and Safety'*.[2]

Government departments, in co-operation with employers, employees, trade unions, employers' organisations, health professionals and voluntary groups have set several challenging targets as part of *'Securing Health Together'*, to be achieved by 2010:

● 20% reduction in incidence of work-related ill health;

● 20% reduction in ill health to members of the public, caused by work activity;

● 30% reduction in the number of working days lost due to work-related ill health;

● everyone currently not in employment, due to ill health or disability is, where necessary and appropriate, made aware of and offered opportunities to prepare for and find work.

Five Programme Action Groups will identify areas for action under each programme, set targets, identify key partners and initiate action. The five programmes are:

● securing compliance through improvements in the law relating to occupational health. For work-related stress (WRS), this is the work we are undertaking to develop the standards;

● striving for excellence through continuous improvement in occupational health. For the WRS strategy we hope to establish centres of best practice who can share their knowledge with local enterprises;

● obtaining essential knowledge on occupational health. For the WRS strategy we are commissioning research to provide the knowledge we need to underpin the standards;

● ensuring that all interested parties have the necessary competences and skills. For the WRS strategy we are equipping enforcement officers with the skills they need to accurately identify WRS and take appropriate action;

● ensuring that the appropriate support mechanisms are in place to deliver information, advice and other support on occupational health. For WRS we have already started a publicity drive – this guide forms one key strand.

PART 1

Introduction

Who is this guide for?

1 This guide is aimed at managers of staff in organisations that employ 50 or more employees. Your 'unit' means the part of the organisation you are responsible for, however it is named in your organisation.

2 The guide does not cover specific requirements of, for example managers in the armed forces and emergency services, whose workers may be exposed to the risk of work-related post-traumatic stress disorder. This is beyond the scope of the guide.

3 The guide provides practical advice on what managers can do to assess and prevent work-related stress and so comply with health and safety law. However, simply thinking of stress as a health and safety issue would be a mistake. It is a complex subject. Health and safety enforcing authorities are not experts in some of the areas that are covered in the guide. Other sources of advice can be found in the section 'References and further information'.

What is work-related stress?

4 We define work-related stress as 'the adverse reaction people have to excessive pressures or other types of demand placed on them'.

5 This makes an important distinction between the beneficial effects of reasonable pressure and challenge (which can be stimulating, motivating, and can give a 'buzz') and work-related stress, which is the natural but distressing reaction to demands or 'pressures' that the person perceives they cannot cope with at a given time.

Who experiences work-related stress?

6 Everyone can, in principle. No-one is 'immune'. Work-related stress exists where people perceive they cannot cope with what is being asked of them at work.

7   It is important to remember that work-related stress is not an illness, but if it is prolonged or particularly intense, it can lead to increased problems with ill health. For example:
- physical effects:
  - heart disease;
  - back pain, gastrointestinal disturbances and various minor illnesses;
- psychological effects:
  - anxiety and depression.

It can also lead to other behaviours that are not helpful to your health, such as skipping meals, drinking too much caffeine or alcohol and smoking cigarettes.

8   Work-related stress can also have consequences for organisations. It may lead to:
- an increase in sickness absence, which can have a domino effect – one person goes off sick which leads to their workload being shared among the remaining staff. They in turn may then be unable to cope, which could affect their health, and lead to greater sickness absence;
- reduced staff morale;
- reduced staff performance; and
- staff seeking alternative employment. Organisations then have the expense of recruiting, inducting, and training new members of staff.

Why organisations should take action

9   There are three broad reasons why employers should take action to tackle work-related stress – ethical, legal and economic.

The ethical argument

10   We have seen that work-related stress can lead to ill health and can seriously affect the quality of life of your workforce. We do not believe that there are any employers in Great Britain who, knowing this, would not wish to do as much as they reasonably can to control the risk.

The legal case

11 The law requires you to tackle work-related stress. In part, health and safety law requires this action, but stress is not just a health and safety issue. While paragraphs 12–13 describe specific pieces of health and safety law relevant to tackling work-related stress, there are other pieces of law that may apply. For example:

- The Employment Rights Act 1996;[3]
- The Public Order Act 1986;[4]
- The Protection from Harassment Act 1997;[5]
- The Working Time Regulations 1998;[6] and
- The Disability Discrimination Act 1995.[7]

Health and safety law

12 Under the *Health and Safety at Work etc Act 1974*[8] employers have a general duty to ensure, so far as is reasonably practicable, the health of their employees at work. This includes taking steps to make sure they do not suffer stress-related illness as a result of their work.

13 Similarly, employers must take account of the risk of stress-related ill health when meeting their legal obligations under the *Management of Health and Safety at Work Regulations 1999*.[9] The main provisions of these Regulations as far as stress is concerned are:

- regulation 3 (duty to assess);
- regulation 4 and Schedule 1 (duty to apply the principles of prevention);
- regulation 13 (duty to ensure employees' capability and to provide training); and
- regulation 19 (duties towards young people).

The economic argument

14 The true cost of work-related stress is not known because it is so complex. However, even if we look at just one element of the cost, sickness absence, we know that it is extremely high. HSE estimates that 6.5 million working days were lost in Britain in 1995 due to stress, depression, anxiety or a physical condition ascribed to work-

related stress – with an average of 16 days off work for each person suffering from the condition. This means that the cost to employers of work-related stress was around £370 million and to society about £3.75 billion (1995/96 prices). These estimates are based on a number of assumptions, and are only intended to be broadly indicative of the costs.

15 But you do not have to look at the total cost to the economy to see how work-related stress can have a huge impact on your unit. Resources are scarce and losing one member of your team because of a stress-related illness can have a dramatic impact on the workload of the rest of the unit.

16 Finally, recent research[10] has shown that having effective people management and development policies and practices are key drivers for good performance and productivity. Having a positive, satisfied, and psychologically healthy workforce will produce economic benefits for your organisation, because of improved attendances, motivation and commitment. Managing work-related stress and securing the well-being of your workforce is an investment.

PART 2

What you must do

Identifying the hazards and taking action

17 Regulation 3 of the Management of Health and Safety at Work Regulations 1999 requires employers to assess risks to health and safety from the hazards of work. This includes the risk of employees developing stress-related illness because of their work. Undertaking a risk assessment for work-related stress is more complicated than for physical hazards, but it involves the same basic principles and process. This guide will help you and your employees work together to devise an effective WRS risk assessment for your organisation.

What does risk assessment mean?

18 The purpose of carrying out a risk assessment is to find out whether existing control measures preventing harm are sufficient, or if more should be done. Completing a risk assessment will not itself reduce work-related stress. However, the actions you take as a result should do so.

Steps to take before undertaking the assessment

19 Doing the following may help you get ready to undertake the assessment:
- talk to all your staff about work-related stress and explain that you want to identify if there is a problem in your unit;
- explain that you are setting up a group to help you (which includes trades union/employee representatives, your unit's health and safety officer (if you have one), one or more supervisors or managers in your unit to co-ordinate action, and, if available, someone from your occupational health service);
- share what you are trying to achieve with staff and then the group and explain that the first step is to undertake a risk assessment;
- ask the group to undertake the assessment using the five steps listed in paragraph 22;
- agree a date by when you want to see the key findings of the risk assessment.

20 Remember, the Safety Representatives and Safety Committees Regulations 1977, the Offshore Installations (Safety Representatives and Safety Committees) Regulations 1989 and the Health and Safety (Consultation with Employees) Regulations 1996 require you to consult with your employees or their representatives on any matter that affects their health or safety at work. This includes the actions you intend to take to tackle work-related stress.

The risk assessment process

21 Paragraphs 24–93 will help your risk assessment group examine the seven elements of work associated with work-related stress.

22 The process follows the principles laid out in HSE's publication *5 steps to risk assessment*.[11] The five steps are:
- identify the hazards;
- decide who might be harmed and how;
- evaluate the risk by:
  - identifying what action you are already taking;
  - deciding whether it is enough; and
  - if it is not, deciding what more you need to do;
- record the significant findings of the assessment; and
- review the assessment at appropriate intervals.

23 If you are starting from scratch, following the 'five steps' principles may save you time. Alternatively, you can dip in and out of the guide for information and advice or create your own systems for action. Your organisation may also have established its own template, which you may be able to adapt and implement at a unit level.

Identify the hazards

How to find out if there is a problem

24 There are seven broad categories of risk factors for work-related stress: culture; demands; control; relationships; change; role; and support, training and factors unique to the individual.

25 We describe these in more detail in Step 3. But, since you need to look for them when you are identifying the hazard, a good working description is:

- **Factor 1:** *Culture* – of the organisation and how it approaches work-related stress;
- **Factor 2:** *Demands* – such as workload and exposure to physical hazards;
- **Factor 3:** *Control* – how much say the person has in the way they do their work;
- **Factor 4:** *Relationships* – covering issues such as bullying and harassment;
- **Factor 5:** *Change* – how organisational change is managed and communicated in the organisation;
- **Factor 6:** *Role* – whether the individual understands their role in the organisation; and whether the organisation ensures that the person does not have conflicting roles;
- **Factor 7:** Support, training and factors unique to the individual:
  - *support* – from peers and line management;
  - *training* – for the person to be able to undertake the core functions of the job;
  - *factors unique to the individual* – catering for individual differences.

26 There are several different data that could help you identify, in broad terms, how big a problem work-related stress is in your unit and where the source may be.

Qualitative methods

Informal talks to staff

27 On a daily basis, you can try to find out the mood of individuals or the team. If people seem continually unhappy, are not themselves, or are not performing well, ask if there is a problem. This can be done 'off the job', eg during regular team meetings, or 'on the job', in the form of 'walk-throughs' and 'talk-throughs'. A walk-through is just what it says: a manager or supervisor walking through a section and observing work processes to assess whether there are any obvious aspects of the job (the way work is done, the pace of work, or working conditions, etc) which may cause excessive pressure. This is most effective if done in combination with a talk-through. A talk-through involves someone describing what is taking place when a task is being carried out. It can be used to get employees to think about tasks in terms of the potential they have to lead to work-related stress.

Performance appraisal

28 If your organisation has a formal system of performance appraisal, this could offer an opportunity to have a one-to-one discussion about work and to explore whether people in your team are experiencing excessive pressure at work. Use the appraisal interview to discover if people are having difficulty coping. Try to pick up on any changes of mood or noticeable differences in performance and offer the opportunity to discuss these openly.

Focus groups

29 Focus groups are normally made up of around 8–10 people, led by a facilitator, in a one-off discussion on a particular topic. Focus groups allow you to explore issues in considerable depth, and have the advantage that people can bounce ideas off others. Focus groups are particularly useful if you want to find out what specific groups of people think about their working lives.

Managing attendance

30 Many organisations now invite their employees to a 'return-to-work' interview with their line manager following sickness absence. If your organisation does this, use the interview to find out if there is a

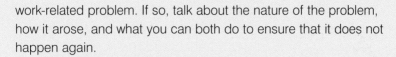

work-related problem. If so, talk about the nature of the problem, how it arose, and what you can both do to ensure that it does not happen again.

31 If the person is suffering from stress because of a non-work-related issue, and does not wish to share their concerns with you, you will have to respect that decision. You may be able to suggest other people they could speak to, such as a trade union representative, a personnel officer, an occupational health professional, an adviser from an employee assistance programme or a colleague or friend. If they are able to share their concerns with you, just try to listen and see if you can help. You may be able to make adjustments to the person's working life in the short term so that they can spend more time resolving personal issues. If you do make adjustments, avoid overloading other members of the team or yourself.

Quantitative methods

32 Your organisation probably collects information that will be useful for your assessment. This could include the following (this is not an exhaustive list).

Sickness/absence data

33 As well as return-to-work interviews it is valuable to take an overview of sickness absence data in your unit. High levels of sickness absence may be an indicator of specific work-related problems. You should investigate the reason for the absences to check whether working conditions are causing increased levels of work-related stress, which in turn is leading to sickness absence.

34 In undertaking an investigation, be aware that stress-related sickness absence is sometimes not reported as such, because of perceived stigma.

Productivity data

35 Where productivity data indicates lower than expected performance (when compared with previous years or against other units), it is worthwhile examining the reasons, through discussions with employees. Working methods or conditions could be causing work-related stress and may be affecting performance.

Turnover

36 If your unit has a higher rate of staff turnover than other units, this may again point to a hidden problem with work-related stress. You could think about holding an 'exit interview' to find out why the person has decided to leave and if work-related stress was a factor. If it was, try to find out the exact cause of the problem and how you can intervene to protect your staff and prevent further losses.

Using a questionnaire

37 You may wish to distribute a questionnaire to find out the scale of the problem in your unit. If so, you should seek specialist advice and think about the pros and cons of using questionnaires, eg:
- pros:
  - they enable you to get views from a wide group of staff;
  - they can give statistically reliable information if you get a good response; and
  - they enable comparison of information year after year, if you ask the same questions;
- cons:
  - responses to questionnaires must be treated confidentially – sharing the results may be difficult;
  - HSE-sponsored research[12] is showing that many of the commercially available questionnaires are not particularly reliable or valid tests for work-related stress. In any case, off-the-shelf questionnaires may not address key issues for your unit. It will often be better to obtain competent advice to help you design a questionnaire that is specific to your unit.

Summary

38 Stress is a very complex issue. Employers should not rely on just one measure of work-related stress, but should try to formulate an overall picture by considering data from several sources. In particular, try to avoid using questionnaires in isolation.

Step 2

Decide who might be harmed and how

Who can be harmed?

39 Work-related stress can affect any member of your team. In particular, it might affect those exposed to the seven factors mentioned in Step 1 (and referred to in more detail in Step 3).

40 At particular times, your staff may be more vulnerable to work-related stress. For example, those returning to work after a stress-related illness, or those who have a domestic crisis, such as a bereavement.

How?

41 The seven risk factors can affect your staff in different ways. For example, some members of your unit may feel anxious about the amount of work they have to do, or the way you will react if they tell you they cannot cope. Finding out how the factors are affecting your unit requires a partnership approach, based on openness, honesty, and trust, which explores what the main effects of work are on staff and what areas should be targeted first.

Evaluate the risk

42 For each of the hazards identified in Step 1, answer the three questions:
- what action are you already taking?
- is it is enough? and
- what more do you need to do?

43 To help you do this, we will go through each of the seven broad risk factors, explaining the type of things you need to think about. When answering the questions, bear in mind that regulation 4 of the Management of Health and Safety at Work Regulations 1999 requires that, in controlling risks, you must apply the principles below in the following order:
- avoid risks (eg make the work environment safer so your staff are not anxious about the threat of violence);
- combat risks at source (eg by organising the work sensibly and giving people clear roles);
- adapt the work to the individual, especially in workplace design, the choice of work equipment and the choice of working methods, to alleviate monotonous work and work at a pre-determined rate, and to reduce their effect on health;
- develop a coherent overall prevention policy which covers technology, organisation of work, working conditions, social relationships and the influence of factors relating to the working environment;
- give collective protective measures priority over individual protective measures (eg by tackling stress at source, rather than just providing information and training to individuals, or access to an Employee Assistance Programme); and
- give appropriate instructions to employees.

Again, you should consult your staff, either directly or through their representatives, to make the most impact in what you do.

44 The seven broad risk factors that follow overlap each other to some extent, and are interrelated in sometimes complex ways. Try to think of the issue of 'job design' as a whole as much as you can. Avoid taking action on one element of work at a time – a total approach, bearing in mind the influence of the other factors, is likely to yield the best result.

Factor 1: Culture

45 Organisational culture is key in determining how successful you will be in managing work-related stress. Organisational culture is often very strong, rooted in history, and difficult to change. A healthy organisational culture will be one where communication, support, and mutual respect are the norm.

46 An organisation has a positive culture when:
- work-related stress and health issues are treated seriously and the organisation responds positively to any concerns;
- there is good, open, communication between employees and between employees and management;
- staff are consulted and, where possible, able to participate in decisions that may affect them;
- staff are supported emotionally and practically;
- staff 'buy into' their work, ie they are undertaking the tasks because they understand what they are trying to achieve and are proud of their achievements for personal and organisational reasons;
- problems are recognised and solved promptly;
- working long hours is not encouraged; and
- staff are not encouraged to take work home.

So: are you doing enough?
If not, here are some ideas:

✔ communicate regularly with your staff, particularly those working remotely and/or from home, and be open and honest about what is happening at work and how this may affect them;

✔ adopt partnership approaches in the workplace to encourage staff to work with you to tackle work-related stress or any emerging business problems. Encourage people to talk to

you at an early stage about work-related stress, mental health issues, and their concerns about work. Create an environment where these issues do not carry stigma;

✔ try to involve your staff in the planning process so that they understand how their work 'fits in';

✔ offer internal support. This could be practical things, like coaching, or it could be emotional support, eg when personal crises such as illness and bereavement, financial worries etc affect your staff.

47 The way you embrace these issues can influence how committed employees feel towards the organisation and how committed they feel the organisation is to their welfare. It can also affect how willing employees are to talk about matters that are causing them genuine concern.

Factor 2: Demands

48 Demands on the individual are often quoted as the main cause of work-related stress. In this section we will look at what that really means and what you can do to ensure that demands do not become unmanageable.

Demands: Work overload

49 Work overload can occur when a person is allocated a great deal of work, but insufficient resources (in terms of ability, staff, time, or equipment) to cope with it.

50 Broadly speaking there are two different types of work overload. Quantitative overload is simply having too much work to do in the time available. Qualitative overload is work that is too difficult for the employee to do, possibly because it is a new area and they have not received appropriate training; or because they do not have the intellectual or physical capacity to do the work; or because they have been set an impossible task (regardless of resource or ability).

51 Employees faced with work overload may try to cope by working excessive hours, which may lead to health problems and problems outside work. Working excessive hours can lead to fatigue, which in turn can impact on performance, creating a 'vicious circle' of more time and effort being put into the work, with less being achieved. Employees may also take work home, which can be detrimental to their family and social life.

52 We also know that work involving a fast pace and the need to resolve conflicting priorities is associated with a higher risk of psychiatric disorder, poor physical fitness or illness. An example is several people giving the same person large amounts of work with short deadlines.

53 On the other hand, it is important to remember that most staff need to have a certain amount of challenge and pressure to keep them interested in the work and motivated. The key is to strike the right balance through discussion with all those involved in the work.

54 There may be occasions when the unit has to work at an extreme level to meet a deadline. When these occasions arise, staff should be told why it is essential to meet the deadline, that their extra efforts are appreciated, and that this will be an infrequent event. Management should consider how to reward their staff after they have made an exceptional effort for the good of the unit.

Capability and capacity

55 Regulation 13(1) of the Management of Health and Safety at Work Regulations 1999 requires employers, when entrusting tasks to employees, to take into account their capabilities as regards health and safety. Paragraph 80 of the Approved Code of Practice on the Regulations says:

'When allocating work to employees, employers should ensure that the demands of the job do not exceed the employees' ability to carry out the work without risk to themselves or others...Employers should review their employees' capabilities to carry out their work, as necessary.'

This includes making sure that employees' mental health is not put at risk through the work they are required to do. Providing adequate training for the job is an important ingredient.

56 You should also pay particular attention to the demands placed on young workers. Regulation 19(2) of the Management of Health and Safety at Work Regulations 1999 prohibits the employment of a young person for work that is beyond his or her psychological capacity; for example, dealing with violent and aggressive behaviour, or having to take decisions under pressure may be work that is beyond a young person's emotional coping ability.

Demands: Work underload

57 The problem here lies with the employee not being sufficiently challenged by work. Job underload, associated with repetitive, routine, boring and under-stimulating work can lead to the employee feeling dissatisfied and under-utilised.

Demands: Physical environment

58 Aspects of the physical environment that can affect employees include noise, vibration, temperature, ventilation, humidity, lighting and hygiene.[13, 14]

59 Some studies[15-17] have shown that employees make a greater number of errors when there are high noise levels, and noise levels have also been found to increase vulnerability to accidents. Exposure to noise is associated with reported fatigue, headaches, irritability and reduced ability to concentrate.

60 In one study,[18] reported stress levels were increased by a combination of different factors, depending on where people were working and the physical environment they were exposed to.

61 Vibration is considered to be a powerful source of stress. It affects brain chemistry and function.[20]

62 In those exposed to harmful substances, fears concerning the effects of these can increase anxiety.

Demands: Psychosocial environment

Violence

63 You should already be assessing the risk of violence to your staff. HSE defines violence as:

'Any incident in which an employee is abused, threatened or assaulted by a member of the public in circumstances arising out of the course of his or her employment.'

64 People who deal directly with the public may face aggressive or violent behaviour. They may be sworn at, threatened or even attacked. This can be a cause of anxiety for your employees (see information sources on violence at work in the 'References and further information' section).

65 Under the Reporting of Injuries, Diseases and Dangerous Occurrences Regulations 1995 employers must notify their health and safety enforcing authority if any act of non-consensual physical violence done to a person at work results in their death, serious injury or incapacity for normal work for three or more days.

So: are you doing enough?
If not, here are some ideas:

✔ ensure there are sufficient resources to do the work allocated:
- if there are insufficient resources, seek guidance from management about priorities;
- support your staff by helping them prioritise, or renegotiate deadlines;
- cover workloads during staff absences;

✔ if people are underloaded, think about giving them more responsibility, but make sure they have been adequately trained;

✔ strike a balance between ensuring that employees are interested and busy, but not underloaded, overloaded, or confused about the job;

✔ train staff so they are able to do their jobs;

✔ encourage staff to talk to you at an early stage if they feel they cannot cope;

✔ talk to your team regularly about what needs to be done, because this can:

- help you understand the challenges the team are currently facing and any pressures they are under;

- find ways of sharing out the work sensibly and agreeing the way forward with the team;

- gain team cohesion and commitment to the work you have planned – if the whole team is aware of what needs to be done and by when, they are likely to be more responsive to you. Allocating more work to a stretched team without explanation is not helpful;

- ensure shift work systems are agreed with staff and that the shifts are fair in terms of workload;

- gain understanding and commitment to unplanned tight deadlines and the exceptional need for long hours;

- help you manage any unexpected absences or losses to the team – everyone knows the key stages of the project and what each other's role is;

✔ lead by example;

✔ have a suitable and sufficient risk assessment to control the physical hazards and risks. Further information on many physical hazards and how you can control them is available from HSE;

✔ assess the risk of physical violence and verbal abuse and take appropriate steps to deal with it.

Factor 3: Control

66 Control is the amount of say the individual has in how their work is carried out. Research[21] has shown that not having much say in how work is done may be associated with poor mental health and a higher risk of alcohol dependency.

67 Research[21] also suggests that when there are greater opportunities for participating in decision-making, greater satisfaction

and higher feelings of self-esteem are reported. Non-participation appears to be linked to work-related stress and overall poor physical health.

> ### So: are you doing enough?
> ### If not, here are some ideas:
>
> ✔ give more control to staff by enabling them to plan their own work, make decisions about how that work should be completed and how problems should be tackled;
>
> ✔ enrich jobs by ensuring that staff are able to use various skills to get tasks completed, and that staff can understand how their work fits in with the wider aims of the unit;
>
> ✔ only monitor employees' output if this is essential. Regular meetings with staff could be arranged to see how things are going. At these meetings managers could provide advice and support where necessary, and ensure that staff are coping;
>
> ✔ a supportive environment is crucial. Staff need to know that managers will support them, even if things go wrong or if they find that they are unable to cope with added pressures.

Factor 4: Relationships

68 We use the term 'relationships' to describe the way we interact with people at work for business purposes.

69 Other people can be important sources of support, but they can also be sources of stress. At work, relationships with bosses, peers and subordinates can dramatically affect the way we feel at the end of the day. There are two particular aspects of relationships that could lead to work-related stress – bullying and harassment.

Bullying and harassment

70 In this guidance, we take 'harassment' to mean unwanted conduct based on sex (including transgender status), race, colour, religion,

nationality, ethnic or national origin or disability that affects the dignity of people at work.

71 In this guidance, we take bullying to mean persistent unacceptable behaviour (or a single, grossly unacceptable, act) by one or more individuals working in the organisation against one or more employees. This behaviour is perceived by the person experiencing it to be offensive, abusive, intimidating, malicious, insulting or involving an abuse of power. It includes:

● any act or threat of physical violence; and
● repeated:
  ● verbal abuse (including shouting or swearing);
  ● insubordination;
  ● victimisation, humiliation or ridicule;
  ● libel, slander or malicious gossip;
  ● spying, pestering, or other inappropriate intrusive questioning, particularly into personal or domestic life;
  ● setting impossible or arbitrary objectives or deadlines;
  ● excessive supervision;
  ● unjustified faultfinding;
  ● withholding information that the employee has a reasonable expectation of being given, exclusion from meetings that the employee has a reasonable expectation of attending or other forms of unreasonable ignoring of the employee;
  ● refusing without reasonable cause reasonable requests for leave or training; or
  ● maliciously preventing career development.

72 Bullying and harassment are two forms of behaviour that are unacceptable in organisations and almost inevitably generate stress and can lead to stress-related illnesses.

So: are you doing enough?
If not, here are some ideas:

✔ work in partnership with staff to ensure that bullying and harassment never emerge as an issue. One way of doing this is by having procedures in place, such as disciplinary and grievance

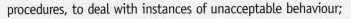

procedures, to deal with instances of unacceptable behaviour;

✔ in consultation with staff and trade unions, draw up effective policies to reduce or eliminate harassment and bullying;

✔ communicate the policies and make it clear that senior management fully supports them;

✔ communicate the consequences of breaching the policies;

✔ create a culture where members of the team trust each other and can be themselves while they are at work;

✔ encourage your staff to recognise the individual contributions of other team members and the benefits of the whole team pulling together.

Factor 5: Change

73 Many organisations have undergone significant change in the last decade or so. They have had to adapt the way they work to accommodate, for example, new technology, competition and changing market conditions. Often their response has included restructuring, downsizing and adopting entirely new ways of working. Poor management of change can lead to individuals feeling anxious about their employment status, and reporting work-related stress.

74 Change can be a stop-start event. That is, the organisation may have a clear objective for a change and securing that objective marks the end of the change process. However, many organisations make more subtle, frequent, changes that can affect staff just as much as a large-scale change, if not properly managed.

So: are you doing enough?
If not, here are some ideas:

✔ explain what the organisation wants to achieve and why it is essential that the change takes place – explain the timetable for action and what the first steps are going to be. Talk about

what the change will mean in terms of day-to-day activity and discuss whether there are any new training needs;

✔ communicate new developments quickly to avoid the spread of rumours in the organisation. If the organisation is planning a major change your staff are likely to be discussing job security, whether they will need to relocate, and whether their terms and conditions will change;
-    face-to-face communication is generally best so that people have the opportunity to ask questions and say what they feel, but any means, eg paper or electronic, would be helpful;
-    have an 'open door' policy where staff can talk to you about their concerns or any suggestions they have for improving the way the change is managed;

✔ give staff the opportunity to comment and ask questions before, during, and after the change;

✔ involve staff in discussions about how jobs might be developed and changed and in generating ways of solving problems;

✔ supporting your staff is crucial during a change;

✔ help staff who are to be made redundant by the change by giving them the skills they need to find a new job, eg by helping them to write a CV and prepare for interviews;

✔ after the change, think about revising work objectives to avoid role conflict and role ambiguity which can, as we will see in paragraphs 76–78, cause work-related stress;

✔ revise your risk assessment to see if any changes eg a decrease in staff numbers, have resulted in increased hazards to staff. Remember that social changes (eg if staff are now working with a completely different group of people) may have more of an impact on the individual than technological or geographical changes.

Factor 6: Role

75 You can help to reduce stress by ensuring that a person's role in the organisation is clearly defined and understood, and that the expectations placed on them do not conflict. There are two potentially stressful areas associated with a person's role in an organisation. They are 'role conflict' and 'role ambiguity'.

Role conflict

76 Role conflict exists when an individual is torn by conflicting job demands or by doing things he or she does not really want to do, or things which the individual does not believe are part of their job. Workers may often feel themselves torn between two groups of people who demand different types of behaviour, or who believe the job entails different functions.

Role ambiguity

77 Role ambiguity arises when individuals do not have a clear picture about their work objectives, their co-workers' expectations of them, and the scope and responsibilities of their job. Often this ambiguity results simply because a manager or supervisor has never adequately explained what is required of them or because the job has changed without this being acknowledged in the job description.

78 A wide range of situations can create role ambiguity. For example, entering a new job or organisation, a promotion or transfer, a new boss, the first supervisory responsibility, or adapting to a change in the structure of the existing organisation.

> ### So: are you doing enough? If not, here are some ideas:
>
> ✔ make sure your staff have a clearly defined role, eg through a personal work plan which enables them to understand exactly what their roles and responsibilities are;
>
> ✔ encourage your staff to talk to you at an early stage if they are not clear about priorities or the nature of the task to be undertaken;

✔ talk to all your staff regularly to make sure that they are completely clear about the current job, what it entails, what you expect of them and what they can expect from you;

✔ make sure that new members of staff receive a comprehensive induction to your organisation. If this is not arranged centrally, you should do it locally;

✔ if your organisation has gone through change, check with members of your team to make sure they understand their new roles and are comfortable with them.

Factor 7: Support, training and factors unique to the individual

79 Regulation 13 of the Management of Health and Safety at Work Regulations 1999 says that every employer should provide adequate health and safety training, but we also recommend that members of staff receive sufficient training to undertake the core functions of their jobs.

80 Your staff need to be competent and feel comfortable doing their jobs. You should provide training (either in-house or externally) to equip staff with the skills they need. If you take on a new piece of work, make sure that the objectives can be achieved using the skills and competencies your staff have, or that could be developed quickly.

81 If you are recruiting new members of staff make sure, as far as you can, that they are matched to the job (in terms of skills, ability, and commitment), receive an induction, and are aware of your policy on work-related stress.

82 The way you support both new and existing staff is key to reducing, or moderating, work-related stress. The way you provide that support can vary from offering help in times of crisis, through to informally congratulating a member of the team for a job well done.

83 Social support at work is also important. The Whitehall II Study of 'Work related factors and ill health'[21] in civil servants found that low social support at work was associated with poor mental health, poor health functioning and increased sickness absence. However high social support at work had a protective effect, being associated with reduced risk of both short and long spells of sickness absence.

84 Even when the work has not been completed to the standard you required, you should attempt to provide constructive, supportive, advice. For example, you can provide advice on where things went wrong and what you would like to see happen in the future. Simply reprimanding your staff and doing nothing else is unlikely to be helpful – your staff will not learn anything and are likely to be anxious about undertaking similar tasks in the future.

85 Finally, you need to take account of the 'make-up' of your team. For example, some members may thrive on working to tight deadlines, others may like to plan their work so that they know what they have to do and when. Try, as far as possible, to cater for these individual differences by talking to your staff as a team – you might find that there is scope to allocate the work in a way that suits all team members, or that you can manage the work in a different way for different people.

86 Do not try to train staff to become 'stress-resistant'. There is little evidence it works, but even so, stress management is not the answer – stress prevention is.

> ## So: are you doing enough?
> ## If not, here are some ideas:
>
> ✔ give support and encouragement to staff, even when things go wrong;
>
> ✔ listen to your staff and agree a course of action for tackling any problems – it is important for staff to feel that the contribution they make at work is valued;
>
> ✔ involve your staff – they need to 'do their bit' to identify problems and work towards agreed solutions;
>
> ✔ encourage staff to share their concerns about work-related stress at an early stage;

✔ provide your staff with suitable and sufficient training to do their jobs;

✔ give new staff a proper induction into the unit and organisation;

✔ take into account that people's skills and the way they approach the work will differ;

✔ value diversity – don't discriminate against people on grounds of race, sex or disability or other irrelevant reasons;

✔ encourage a healthy 'work-life balance' (see the 'References and further information' section for a contact for more information);

✔ encourage staff to take their annual leave entitlement and their meal breaks.

Step 4

Record the significant findings of the assessment

87 The Management of Health and Safety at Work Regulations 1999 require you to undertake a 'suitable and sufficient' risk assessment. You need to cover the main hazards (for example, if you are undertaking a large change), not every single thing.

88 Regulation 3(6) of the Regulations requires that, if the employer employs five or more employees, they must record: (a) the significant findings of the assessment; and (b) any group of employees identified by it as being especially at risk. These findings should be shared with employees.

89 An employer with fewer than five employees does not have to record the main findings of the risk assessment. However, for review purposes, it would be a good idea to do so, since you still have to share the findings with employees.

90 You should share the findings of the assessment with your staff.

Review the assessment at appropriate intervals

91 Regulation 3(3) of the Management of Health and Safety at Work Regulations 1999 says you must review your assessment whenever there is reason to think it is no longer valid. At first, review the assessment every six months. If after a year this period is too frequent (ie there are no significant changes), then move to an annual review period. You should engage your employees or their representatives in this process.

92 You should also revise your assessment if you become aware of events on the horizon that could affect employees – a change in senior management, or a merger, for example. Repeat the risk assessment process, again in consultation with your employees.

93 Finally, if you become aware of changes in a person's domestic life you should try to consider how this may affect the risk assessment. Further information on dealing with factors out of your control is given in paragraphs 94–101.

Work-related stress risk assessment: *Summary*

Step   *Action*

1   **Looking for the hazards – the main types of hazards can be grouped into seven broad categories.**

Factor 1: Culture (paragraphs 45–47)
Factor 2: Demands (paragraphs 48–65)
Factor 3: Control (paragraphs 66–67)
Factor 4: Relationships (paragraphs 68–72)
Factor 5: Change (paragraphs 73–74)
Factor 6: Role (paragraphs 75–78)
Factor 7: Support, training and factors unique to the individual (paragraphs 79–86)
You should use a mixture of qualitative and quantitative data-gathering methods. Only use questionnaires with great care.

2   **Decide who might be harmed and how.**

Any of your staff, regardless of age, status, gender, ethnicity, or disability, can be affected by work-related stress. However, some people may be at higher risk at different times, for example young workers.

3   **Evaluate the risk and decide if enough is being done.**

Consider how likely it is that each hazard mentioned in Step 1 could cause harm in your unit.
In taking action ask yourself:
● what action is already being taken?
● is it enough?
● if not, what more will you do?
Remember that you should try to eliminate the risks as far as possible. You should try to combat risks at an organisational level at source before considering the training (in terms of pressure management) or counselling needs of the individual member of staff. You should try to take action that protects everyone, rather than just a few individuals.

4   **Record your findings.**

If your organisation employs five or more people, you must record the main findings of your risk assessment and should share the findings with employees.

You should use the this document to monitor progress and help you keep an eye on particular hazards.

In organisations with fewer than five employees, recording the findings is not legally required, although you may find it helpful to write down the key findings of your assessment since you still have to share the findings with employees.

5   **Review your assessment and revise where necessary.**

Review your assessment whenever significant changes occur in the organisation, or in the way your unit handles its business. Do this in consultation with employees. Consider reviewing the assessment regularly.

What about the factors out of your control?

94 It is important to recognise that work-related stress is often the result of the combined effect of a number of different factors, such as workload, the degree of control people have over their work, relationships at work, etc.

95 This guide has focused on the work-related elements of stress, not the other aspects of people's lives. When tackling work-related stress it is important to recognise employees as whole people and to acknowledge that problems in someone's domestic life do not necessarily stay at home. Staff can be affected by outside events while at work and we hope that this guidance will encourage you and your staff to discuss any matters that may affect performance while at work. A flexible approach is needed to tackle this complicated issue.

96 If you do not feel as though you are able to help your staff during difficult domestic times, you may be able to refer them to your organisation's welfare service who may be able to help with issues which may be causing anxiety. If your organisation doesn't have a welfare service, think about asking either the trades union representative, or local voluntary support groups, for advice.

Internal factors

97 If you discover that the main problem lies with a centrally managed issue, such as the promotion system, then take the issue further up the line. You are likely to find that your staff will benefit from knowing that you will take up issues on their behalf, even if you do not succeed in changing the organisation's policy.

98 There may be other internal issues that are affecting your staff and causing them anxiety. For example, they may not be able to assert themselves and are continually taking on more work than they can manage. If you find this is the case when you undertake your risk assessment, you could offer training (on the job, or an external course) to help them develop the skills they need. In the meantime, you could support the member of staff and continually monitor and review their workload.

External factors

99 Regular communication can also help overcome any anxiety your staff have about external factors that are affecting, or could affect, the organisation. For example, new regulations that are coming into force, a competitor, or a national crisis.

The work-life balance

100 Flexibility in your employment practices can help you increase productivity, attract the skilled, experienced and motivated staff you need – and retain them in a competitive marketplace. It is about giving people working options that fit in with your business needs – and that may relieve potential stresses on your employees to produce a more focused, committed team.

101 The Government has produced specific guides on striking the right work-life balance. Contact details on where you can get these guides are given in the 'References and further information' section.

PART 3

Caring for those with work-related stress

I know some of my team are reporting work-related stress. What can I do?

102 Despite the precautions you have taken in Part 2, you may find that a member of the unit is experiencing work-related stress. The following section provides some general advice on the things you can do to ensure that you are comfortable dealing with the person, and that they know you care for their well-being.

How you can help

Things about you

● You should develop the skills you need to deal with stressed and distressed members of staff, and talk about any identified needs with your superior (who in turn needs to think about their training needs).

● Try not to be panicked by emotion. Acceptance, reassurance and a calm, measured response will be helpful. Ask if there is anyone the person wants to have contacted (if it seems appropriate).

Things you can do

● Ensure that you do not penalise employees for feeling the effects of too much pressure.

● Positively encourage staff to manage their own well-being at work, and provide them with the support they need to do this. Managers need to respond helpfully to members of staff who are going through stressful times. Simply listening to people can help.

● You could ask the person how you can help rather than just assuming a particular course of action is best. Even in acute distress people can have a clear sense of their own needs. You may wish to note the agreed action points for ease of reference.

- At a suitable time, explore whether work is a factor and ensure the person knows what kind of support the organisation can offer.

- Discuss whether any changes in workload or other adjustments would help. Talk about any resources the organisation has that can help, eg an employee assistance service, other access to counselling, a confidential talk with a member of staff who is not their supervisor, etc.

- Try to create a culture and structures that enable members of staff to seek help and manage their own support needs.

Rehabilitation

How can you help?

- Ensure there are arrangements for staff to have an early return-to-work interview. At that interview, focus on the person rather than on any work problems that arose due to an absence.

- Make sure that people who have been off sick with a stress-related illness feel that they are welcome back.

- Make sure that the person is not placed in a situation which contains the same factors that led to their illness.

- If you discover that work caused, or was part of the cause, of the ill health leading to absence, you should address the problems and make alterations.

- Your staff are likely to feel uncomfortable if they think that you are giving them special treatment or are not giving them enough to do. Make sure that the person undertakes the range of duties you would expect a person in that job to do, but reduce those elements of work that were excessive and led to illness. If feasible, you could offer to reduce responsibilities in the short-term, or offer part-time working, to gradually phase the person back into work.

References
and further information

References

1 *Securing health together: A long-term occupational health strategy for England, Scotland, and Wales* MISC225 HSE Books 2000

For further information on the Occupational Health Strategy and its Partnership Board visit the Occupational Health Strategy website: www.ohstrategy.net

2 *Revitalising Health and Safety: Strategy Statement* The Department of the Environment, Transport and the Regions 2000

Available from: The Department of the Environment, Transport and the Regions, Free Literature Service, PO Box 236, Wetherby, West Yorkshire, LS23 7NB Tel: 0870 1226236 Fax: 0870 1226237

3 *The Employment Rights Act 1996* HMSO 1996 ISBN 0 10 541896 X

4 *The Public Order Act 1986* HMSO 1996 ISBN 0 10 546486 4

5 *Protection from Harassment Act 1997* TSO 1997 ISBN 0 10 544097 3

6 *The Working Time Regulations 1998* TSO 1998 ISBN 0 11 079410 9

7 *Disability Discrimination Act 1995* HMSO 1996 ISBN 0 10 545095 2

8 *Health and Safety at Work etc Act 1974* HMSO 1974 ISBN 0 10 543774 3

9 *Management of health and safety at work. Management of Health and Safety at Work Regulations 1999. Approved Code of Practice and guidance* L21 HSE Books 2000 ISBN 0 7176 2488 9

10 Patterson, MG, West, MA, Hawthorn, R et al *Impact of people management practices on business performance.* Institute of Personnel and Development 1997 ISBN 0 85292 725 8

11   *5 steps to risk assessment* INDG163(rev1) HSE Books 1998 Single copies free, also available in priced packs, ISBN 0 7176 1565 0

12   *A critical review of psychosocial hazard measures* Due to be published Summer 2001 by HSE Books

13   Levi, L *Stress in industry: Causes, effects and prevention* OSH Series No.51 International Labour Office 1984 ISBN 9 22103539 5

14   Manninen,O 'Changes in subjective stressfulness under various combinations of noise, vibration, temperature and work tasks' *Archives of Complex Environmental Studies* 1990 2 (1) 25-30

15   Powell, PI, Hale, M, Martin, J et al *Two thousand accidents: A shop floor study of their causes* Report No 21 Institute of Industrial Psychology, London 1971

16   *Stress research and stress management: Putting theory to work* CRR61 HSE Books 1993 ISBN 0 7176 0684 8

17   Ronayne, T, McDonald, N J, Smith, H V *Noise, stress and work* EF/81/06 European Foundation for the Improvement of Living and Working Conditions 1981

18   Elo, A L 'Health and stress of seafarers' *Scandinavian Journal of Work, Environment and Health* 1985 11 (6) 427-432

19   Taguchi, T, Inagaki, H, Nagai, T, and Ishikawa, H, 'Influence of Vertical Vibration on Driver Stress Assessed by Stress Hormones', in *From Experience to Innovation* - IEA '97, Proceedings of the 13th Triennial Congress of the International Ergonomics Association, Tampere, Finland June 29-July 4, 1997, Seppala et al (editors), Finnish Institute of Occupational Health, Helsinki, Volume 6

20   Johanning, E, Wilder, D G, Landrigan, PJ et al 'Whole-body vibration exposure in subway cars and review of adverse health effects', *Journal of Occupational Medicine* 1991 33 (5) 605-612

21   *Work-related factors and ill health: The Whitehall II study* CRR266 HSE Books 2000 ISBN 0 7176 1784 X

While every effort has been made to ensure the accuracy of the references listed in this leaflet, their future availability cannot be guaranteed.

TSO and HMSO publications are available from The Publications Centre, PO Box 276, London SW8 5DT Tel: 0870 600 5522 Fax: 0870 600 5533 Website: www.clicktso.com (They are also available from bookshops.)

HSE priced and free publications are available by mail order from HSE Books (see details on inside back cover).

Further information

If you would like to know more about the Commission's strategy for tackling work-related stress, Securing Health Together, or health and safety law, contact HSE's InfoLine Tel: 08701 545500 Fax: 02920 859260 e-mail: hseinformationservices@natbrit.com or write to HSE Information Services, Caerphilly Business Park, Caerphilly CF83 3GG. You can also visit HSE's website: www.hse.gov.uk

HSE and general information

General advice on health and safety issues is available from:
Your local HSE inspector or HSE Employment Medical Advisory Service (listed under 'Health and Safety Executive' in the phone book).

Your local authority inspector (listed under 'Local Authorities' in the phone book).

Mental health

Advice on all aspects of mental health is available from:

In England:
Health Development Agency, Trevelyan House,
30 Great Peter Street, London SW1P 2HW Tel: 020 7413 1991

In Scotland:
Health Education Board for Scotland, Woodburn House,
Canaan Lane, Edinburgh EH10 4SG Tel: 0131 536 5500

In Wales:
The National Assembly for Wales, Health Promotion Division,
Cathays Park, Cardiff CF10 1NQ Tel: 029 20 825111

For further information on helping people who are diagnosed with a mental illness contact:
MIND (National Association for Mental Health), Granta House, 15–19 Broadway, London E15 4BQ
Mindinfoline: 0845 7660163 (outside London)
                      020 8522 1728 (London)
Or Work Net: 020 8215 2444

If you do want to recruit a consultant to help you assess levels and sources of stress in your organisation, the British Psychological Society can provide you with details of occupational psychologists and consultants:
British Psychological Society, St Andrews House, Leicester LE1 7DR
Tel: 0116 254 9568 www.bps.org.uk

Equal opportunities

For further information on equal opportunities contact
The Equal Opportunities Commission, Commission for Racial Equality, or the Disability Rights Commission:
Customer Contact Point, Equal Opportunities Commission, Arndale House, Manchester M4 3EQ Tel: 0161 833 9244
www.eoc.org.uk

Commission for Racial Equality, Elliot House, 10–12 Allington Street, London SW1E 5EH Tel: 0207 828 7022 www.cre.gov.uk

Disability Rights Commission Helpline: 08457 622633
(Minicom: 020 7211 4037)
www.drc-gb.org.uk

Employers Forum on Disability, Nutmeg House,
60 Gainsford St, London SE1 2NY Tel: 020 7315 6157

Counselling and Stress Management Associations

Advice for counselling and stress management is available from:
British Association for Counselling and Psychotherapy
www.counselling.co.uk

International Stress Management Association, Division of Psychology, South Bank University, 103 Borough Road, London SE1 0AA Tel: 07000 780430

Work-life balance

For further information on the work-life balance contact:
For employers in England and Scotland:
Work-life Balance Team, Department for Education and Employment, Level 1, Park Gate, 21 Tothill Street, London SW1H 9LL Tel: 08700 012345 Public Enquiries: 020 7273 5626 www.DFEE.gov.uk/work-lifebalance

For employers in Wales:
Welsh Development Agency, Principality House, The Friary, Cardiff CF10 3FE Tel: 02920 828781

Employment relations

For further information on trade union representation, employee rights, and bullying and harassment at work contact:
TUC, Congress House, Great Russell Street, London WC1B 3LS Tel. 020 7636 4030   www.TUC.org.uk

For further information on performance appraisal, personal work plans, or managing attendance contact:
Chartered Institute of Personnel and Development, CIPD House, Camp Road, London SW19 4UX Tel: 020 8971 9000 www.cipd.co.uk

Information on Employee Assistance Programmes is available from:
UK Employee Assistance Professionals Association, Premier House, 85 High Street, Witney, Oxon OX28 6HY Tel: 0800 7837616

For further information and leaflets on employment rights, good management practices, and bullying and harassment at work contact:
ACAS, Head Office, Brandon House, 180 Borough High Street, London SE1 1LW Tel: 020 7396 5100 www.acas.org.uk

Learning Resource:

Printed and published by the Health and Safety Executive   C300   6/01